Barbie™

Fun To Make

Activity Book

A Dorling Kindersley Book

DK

Dorling Kindersley

LONDON, NEW YORK, SYDNEY, DELHI, PARIS,
MUNICH and JOHANNESBURG

Senior Designer Sarah Ponder
Designer Tanya Tween
Text by Cynthia O'Neill
Editors Cynthia O'Neill, Marie Greenwood
Art Editor Jacquie Gulliver
Managing Editor Karen Dolan
DTP Designer Jill Bunyan, Susan Wright
Production Jo Rooke
Photographer Steve Shott
Designer and modelmaker Katie Sheffer

First published in Great Britain in 2000
by Dorling Kindersley Limited,
9 Henrietta Street, London WC2E 8PS

2 4 6 8 10 9 7 5 3 1

BARBIE and associated trademarks are owned by
and used under licence from Mattel, Inc.
© 2000 Mattel, Inc.
All Rights Reserved.

All rights reserved. No part of this publication may be
reproduced, stored in a retrieval system or transmitted in any
form or by any means, electronic, mechanical, photocopying,
recording or otherwise without the prior written permission
of the copyright owner.

ISBN 0 7513 4533 4

Colour reproduction by Media Development, UK
Printed in L Rex, China

A CIP catalogue record for this book is available from
the British Library.

**The publisher would like to thank the following for their kind
permission to reproduce their photographs:**
Telegraph Colour Library: Bavaria – Bildagentur 43, right;
Bluestone Productions 43, left.

Dorling Kindersley would like to following for their help in making this book:
Ashleigh Frost, Danielle Bromley, Emily Couchman, Esther Templer,
Georgia Richfield, Gregg Richfield, Hannah Mead, Hannah Partridge,
Harriet Forbes Lange, Jessica McKenzie, Katelyn Birchmore,
Lily Dang, O'Shea Pascal, Serena Dwyer, Stephanie Joannou,
Stephanie Spyrakis, Tiffany Simpson, Victoria Cheroomi.

For our complete
catalogue visit
www.dk.com

Contents

Starting off

Hi there! Are you ready to have
fun? Because this book is packed
with ideas for things
to make and do!
Inside, you'll find brilliant
designs for jewellery, delicious
recipes, and wonderful gifts
to make for your friends.
Step-by-step photos and simple
instructions take you through each
stage of the activity. And photos of
the things you need for each project
are shown at the beginning, so you
can gather everything together.
It's easy, when I show you
how – so let's get started!

Barbie ™

A collection of
paints, pens, and
stickers will always
come in handy

The coloured sequins and gems you need can be found at most craft shops

Stationers and big department stores sell many types of paper and card

Golden rules

No matter which project you are trying out, remember to follow the golden rules. It's the best way to make sure you get the most fun from every page!

Before you start any activity, read the instructions all the way through.

! Be careful! Don't use sharp knives or scissors unless a grown-up is there to help you work safely.

Keep clean! Wear an apron, tie back long hair, and always wash your hands before you cook.

Work at a wipe-clean surface, or put newspaper down on the table before you start an activity.

Junk jewellery!

It's easy to create fantastic jewellery from household junk. All you need is a little imagination! Read on to learn how to turn foil wrappers into a sweetheart pendant, or spare buttons into a colourful necklace. There's even a clever idea for turning the lid from a washing-up bottle into a glittering ring, with a secret compartment!

You will need

Foil or plastic sweet wrappers

Safety scissors

Pipecleaners

Sequins

Cotton buds

Card

Felt-tip pen

Glue stick

Ribbons, at least 50 cm long

Sweetheart pendant

1 Draw a heart shape, about 8 cm across at the widest point, onto thickish card. Cut it out.

2 Flatten out the sweet wrappers. Cut them into 2 cm squares – take care not to tear them!

3 Glue the squares of sweet wrapper onto the card heart, making a pretty check pattern.

4 If the squares of foil overlap the edges of the card heart, fold them over neatly and stick them down on the back.

5 Bend a pipe cleaner so it is the same size and shape as the heart. Glue it to the card.

Barbie says:

Always take care when you are using scissors!

6 With a cotton bud, dot a little glue onto a sequin. Glue a sequin neatly in the middle of each square, to finish off.

Tape your pendant to a pretty ribbon

Why not try different shapes, like this flowery pendant?

Secrets ring

Glue

Small photo of a pet or friend

Craft ring

Washing-up liquid bottle lid

1 Pull the lid from an old washing-up liquid bottle (you may need to ask a grown-up for help).

2 Put the lid on top of some thin card and draw around it. Cut out the circle you have made.

3 Use strong glue to stick the card into the bottom of the washing-up bottle lid. (The card should fit tightly.)

4 Now put a drop of the strong glue onto the flat top of the craft ring. Stick the ring to the card inside the lid.

5 Decorate the top of the lid-ring with a glittery or flowery sticker.

6 Fold the small picture into a thin strip, then slip it inside the secret compartment of the ring. Now it's ready to wear!

Only you will know the secret!

Bright as a button!

Buttons

Tape measure

Elastic thread

Nail polish

Beads

1 Measure around your neck. Cut some elastic thread, three times longer than this measurement.

2 Fold the elastic in half. Tie a knot in the folded end, to make a small loop, as shown here.

3 Paint the cut ends of the elastic with clear nail polish. This will stop them fraying and make it easier to thread the beads.

4 Thread colourful beads and buttons onto the elastic, putting one strand of elastic through each button hole.

Barbie says:

Make a button bracelet, too. Use a shorter length of elastic thread and follow steps 2 to 6!

5 Build the buttons and beads into a multi-coloured design, until you have almost reached the end of the elastic thread.

6 Knot the loose ends and put the knotted end through the loop. Tie this. Slip the necklace over your head.

Terrific tiara

I feel like a princess in a fairy-tale when I wear a tiara. Now you will, too, when you make the terrific tiara on these pages! It's covered with spangles, glitter and stars, and is perfect for a special occasion, a fancy dress party, or just dressing up with your friends. And the best thing about this tiara is – it's fun to make!

You will need

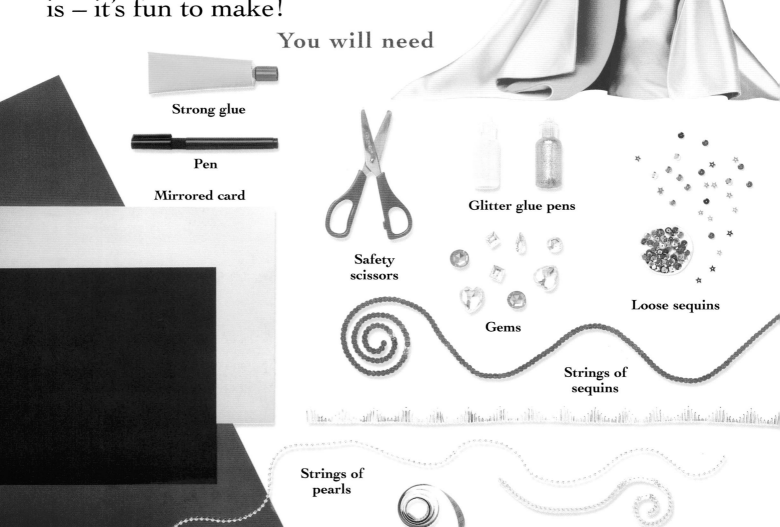

Strong glue

Pen

Mirrored card

Safety scissors

Glitter glue pens

Loose sequins

Gems

Strings of sequins

Strings of pearls

Tape measure

1 Cut out a long strip of mirrored card, about 2 cm wide and 60 cm long. Put this to one side.

2 Draw a front for the tiara, about 20 cm x 6.5 cm, on the back of the mirrored card. Cut it out.

3 Use strong glue to stick sequins and beads in a pretty pattern over the front of the card.

Fit for a Princess

4 Once the glue is dry, put more glue on the back of the card. Stick it to the long strip.

You may need to bend the tiara to the shape of your head

5 Glue the ends of the strip together, so that the tiara will sit snugly on top of your head.

Tiara styles

You can change the style of your tiara by cutting out different shapes. Here are some of my favourites.

Spiky

Smooth

Wavy

Flower power

You can make beautiful presents or cards, or create a pretty secrets diary, by pressing the flowers and leaves that grow in your garden. It's simple, when I show you how! Remember, the easiest flowers to press are the ones with flat faces – pansies or flat-faced roses are just right.

You will need

A mix of flowers, such as here

Gerbera

Clear, sticky-backed plastic

Roses

Ivy leaves

Cotton buds

Silver card and stickers

Strong glue

Dried grasses

Hole punch

Thin card

Paintbrush

Verbena

Felt-tip pen

Wrapping paper

Poster paint

Pressing fresh flowers

1 Find a heavy book (a dictionary is good). Measure the width and height of the open pages.

2 Cut a piece of blotting paper to the size of the open pages. Lay the folded paper on the book.

3 Choose the mix of flowers you want to press. Snip off the stems with some safety scissors.

Barbie says:
Make sure you leave the flowers to dry for at least four weeks!

4 Lay flowers and leaves on top of the blotting paper. Only use the right-hand side of the book.

5 Arrange flower petals elsewhere in the book. Close it, and stack a pile of heavy books on top.

Beads

Safety scissors

Ruler

Long satin ribbons

Heavy books

Blotting paper

Ribbon

Coloured writing paper

Once you've piled the heavy books on top, leave your flowers to press for one month

Bookmark

1 Draw a narrow strip, 12 x 5 cm, on thin card. End it in a point, like an arrow, and cut out.

2 Use watercolour paints to begin your design. Why not start it with a stem and some leaves?

3 Use a cotton bud to dab glue onto the pressed flowers. Stick them to the card in a pretty pattern.

4 To protect the flowers, cover the bookmark with clear sticky-backed plastic, measuring about 18 x 8 cm.

5 Glue your flower design onto a thicker piece of silver card.

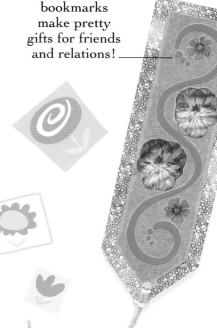

These flowery bookmarks make pretty gifts for friends and relations!

6 To finish off your bookmark, make a hole in the tip. Thread a ribbon, strung with beads, through the hole.

Use the ribbon to fix the tag to your gift

Keep your design simple

Barbie says:
Adapt these steps and use a small square or circle of card, to make a special gift tag!

Secrets diary

1 Choose two pieces of thick, pretty, pink card. Cut each one to measure about 30 x 21 cm.

2 Line up the cards. With a holepunch, make two holes in the left-hand side.

3 Cut some silver card, 27 x 18 cm, for the front of your diary. Glue it to a piece of pink card.

4 Make a flower picture. Stick pressed flowers and rose petals onto plain card. Why not include stickers or beads as well?

5 When your design is finished, cover the picture with a piece of clear, sticky-backed plastic to protect it.

6 Glue the flowery picture to the front cover of your diary.

7 Make the inside pages by cutting rectangles of paper just smaller than the covers. Punch holes in the side of the pages.

8 Put the paper inside the card covers, with the holes lined up. Tie ribbons through the holes, to hold the book together.

Pretty plaits

Trying a new hairstyle is great fun. Here is one of my favourite ways to create a completely different look – pretty plaits!

Follow these simple steps to make a basic plait. Then you can have a wonderful time trying lots of new styles, like the ones I've shown on the next page. And here's a great Barbie tip – ask a friend to help you. It's more fun with two or three!

You can choose from

Hairbands

Slides

Flower-shaped hairbands

Butterfly-shaped grips

Hair slides

Brush

Comb

Ribbons

How to make a plait

Divide a ponytail into three equal strands.

Cross the right strand of hair over the middle strand.

Cross over the left strand. Repeat last two steps to end.

Basic plait

1 Comb the hair and pull it into a ponytail (don't pull too tight!). Divide the ponytail into three strands.

2 Lift the right strand. Cross it to the middle, between the other strands of hair. Pull it firm.

3 Cross the left strand into the middle. Repeat 2 and 3 until all the hair is plaited. Tie with a band.

Now try these!

1 Make three thin plaits on each side of the head. Keep them in place with clips and ribbons.

2 Put the hair into two bunches and plait them. Pin to the back of the head for a fun look!

3 Wind a ribbon around one of the strands of hair before you plait it, for an extra-pretty look!

Sparkly clips and flowers

This style suits long hair

Matching hairband and ribbon

Forever flowers!

Make a posy of flowers that will bloom all year round! Pop these paper flowers into a vase (without water!) to brighten up your bedroom with a splash of colour. Or why not make a big bouquet, as a fabulous gift for Mother's Day?

You will need

Glue stick

Fuse wire

Garden wire

Pen

Pencil

Cotton wool balls

Safety scissors

Selection of crêpe papers

Delightful daisy

1 Take a 30 cm length of garden wire. Make a loop at one end and glue cotton wool to the loop.

2 Cover the cotton wool with a square of crêpe paper, 8 x 8 cm. Glue it around the cotton wool.

3 Twist any leftover paper around the garden wire for a neat finish, and glue it down.

4 Cut out two crêpe paper circles, each about 8 cm across. Snip around the edges, making a fringe about 2 cm deep.

5 Thread the fringed circles on the wire stem. (See page 48 for a tip on how to make small holes in paper.)

6 Finally, wrap 10 cm of fuse wire tightly around the wire stem and the base of the petals, to hold them together.

Paper circles

It's easy to draw a circle on crêpe paper. Just trace around a mug, tin or small saucer, then cut it out!

Circle

Try lots of coloured paper – bright yellow and blue for a funky mix!

Pretty in pink – pale colours look sweet!

Sunshine yellow and orange look cheerful together

Pretty posy

1 Take a sheet of pink crêpe paper, 20 x 14 cm, and fold it in half to make a double thickness.

2 Enlarge and copy the posy shape on page 21 onto the top of the paper. (See the tip on page 48.)

3 Cut around the flower outline, through both sheets of paper, to end up with two flower shapes.

4 Thread the deep pink flower shapes onto a ready-made stem (turn back to steps 1 to 3, on page 19, for instructions).

5 To hold your flower together, wind 10 cm of fuse wire tightly and neatly around the petals and the yellow centre.

Barbie says:
Cover a cracker or crisp tin with coloured paper, to make a vase for your paper posy!

Leaves

1 Draw a leaf, 10 cm long, on folded paper (copy shape on page 21). Cut it out, making two leaves.

2 Cover one leaf with glue. Lay a piece of fuse wire, 15 cm long, down the middle.

3 Stick the second leaf on top, covering up the wire. A little fuse wire will be left over.

Finishing off

1 Cut out a long, thin strip of green crêpe paper. It should measure about 2 x 60 cm.

2 Place the green strip on newspaper to protect your table. Then cover the strip with glue.

3 Fix two leaves to the base of each flower, by winding the leftover fuse wire around each stem.

Separate the paper layers to show off the petals

4 Wrap the strip of green paper around the leaves and the stem, until any wire is covered up. Trim the ends neatly.

Pretty posy with stem and leaves

A colourful mix of delightful daisies and pretty posies!

Flower patterns

Trace and enlarge the shapes below, using the tips shown on page 48. Use them as patterns for the flowers and leaves.

Posy

Leaf

Party time!

Next time you give a party, why not make the invitations, decorations and party hats yourself? The day will be even more special if you choose a theme for each guest. Last year, Stacie received a butterfly-shaped party invitation from her friend, Janet. At the party, Stacie was thrilled to have her own butterfly picture-straw to drink from and a butterfly hat to wear!

Come to my party!

You will need

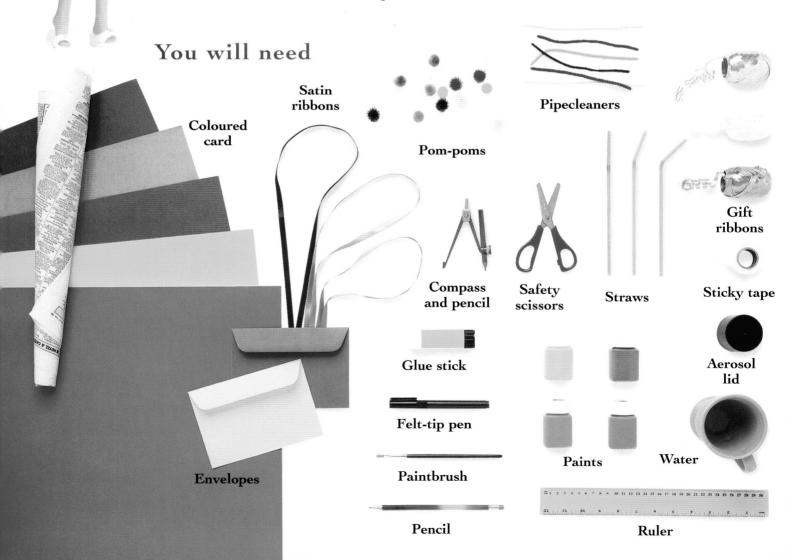

Coloured card

Satin ribbons

Pom-poms

Pipecleaners

Gift ribbons

Compass and pencil

Safety scissors

Straws

Sticky tape

Glue stick

Aerosol lid

Felt-tip pen

Paints

Water

Envelopes

Paintbrush

Pencil

Ruler

Party invitations

1 Fold a strip of paper, 44 x 11 cm, in half and in half again. Open it up and pleat along the folds.

2 Draw a butterfly (or a heart, flower or other design) on the top pleat of coloured paper.

3 Cut out the butterfly – but don't cut round the outline where it overlaps the edge of the paper.

4 Open out the paper. You should find a line of butterflies! Draw fine details onto each one.

5 Now decorate your invitations with paints or stickers.

Barbie says:

Your drawing should fill the space and the edges must overlap the edges of your paper!

Write the details of your party on the back of each invitation

Come to my PARTY!

Picture straws

1 Draw around the lid of an aerosol can onto card to make circles. You need one circle per guest.

2 Draw an animal or a cute bug on each circle (pick different designs for each guest). Paint them.

3 Cut out the pictures. With grown-up help, make little slits in the top and bottom of each one.

4 Push a straw through the bottom slit of each picture and out again through the top slit.

Barbie says:

Write the name of each guest on the back of their picture straw, so they know where to sit at the table.

Add wings and stalks to the card circle to make a buzzy bee!

You won't need to draw a circle to create a colourful butterfly

Make delicious party drinks – see the recipes on page 28

Picture patterns

Here are some ideas for sweet pictures to decorate the drinking straws.

A sunny, smiley daisy for flower girls!

Flower

An adorable kitten

Cat

Party hats

1 Draw a circle, 30 cm across, onto card (see page 48). Cut it out, then cut it in half.

2 Bring the edges of the card together, to make a cone (leaving a small gap at the top). Glue in place.

3 Run curly gift ribbons through the small gap at the top of your hat and tape to inside of hat.

4 Make a small hole on each side of the cone. Thread the holes with silky ribbons and knot these into place.

5 Paint a design on the card (we chose to use butterflies). Cut out. Stick to the hat with glue.

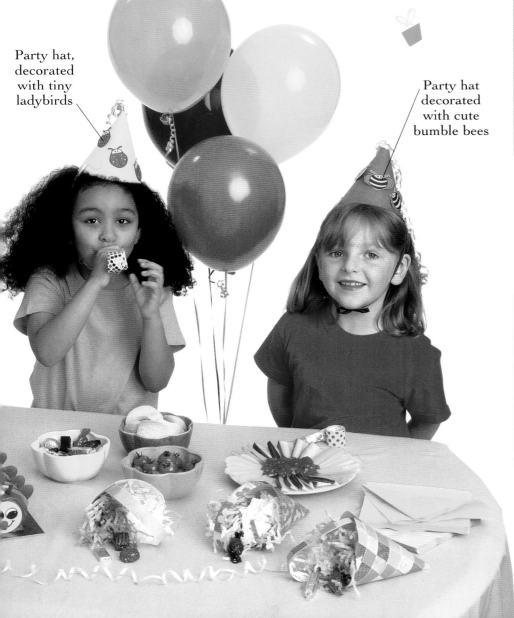

Party hat, decorated with tiny ladybirds

Party hat decorated with cute bumble bees

Cute cakes

I always think the best bit of baking a cake is choosing the yummy decorations to finish it off! These mini-cake treats come in all sorts of shapes, and they're so pretty, too! Serve them next time you have a party or make a few for when friends come to tea.

Now let's get started!

You will need

Teaspoon

Dessertspoon

Small bowls

Sieve

Cake decorations

Plastic bowl

Sweets

Flaked chocolate

Candied fruits

Chopping board

Family-sized sponge

Warm water

Cake cutters

Food colourings

Icing sugar

1 Using different-shaped biscuit cutters, cut lots of mini-cakes from the family-sized sponge cake.

2 Now make glacé icing. Use a sieve to sift the icing sugar into a bowl. This gets rid of lumps.

3 Slowly add drops of warm water and mix it in. Stop when the mixture is fairly runny like glue.

4 Divide the icing into some small bowls and mix a few drops of red or green food colouring into each one.

5 Use the icing at once. Spread it carefully over the cakes and leave to set. Then cover your cakes with decorations!

Try using orange juice, instead of warm water to make an orange-flavoured icing

Use cake toppings, chocolate or sweets to decorate your cute cakes whichever way you want!

Candy Cake

Orange delight

Chocolate star

Hundreds 'n' thousands

Classic heart

Lemon delight

Silver starburst

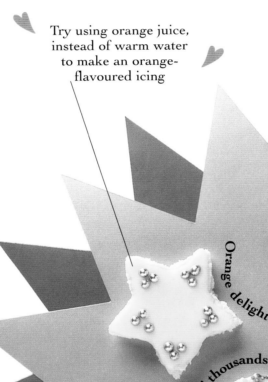

Dreamy drinks

Share delicious drinks with your friends when you make these chocolate ice-cream shakes and frothy fruit ices. For extra fun, serve the drinks in pretty glasses, decorated with fruit, cocktail umbrellas and colourful straws.

Mmm! They're delicious!

You will need

Spoon

Knife

Icecream

Chopping board

Chocolate sauce

Fruits

Milk

Ice-cube tray

Fruit-flavoured squash

Blender

Ingredients

These quantities are to make two drinks, so increase the quantities as necessary.

FRUIT ICE

Selection of soft fruits

Flavoured ice cubes, made with fruit-flavoured squash

CHOCOLATE SHAKE

500g vanilla icecream

2 tablespoons of chocolate sauce

2 cups of milk

NEVER use a blender unless a grown-up is around to WATCH OVER you!

Fruit ice

1 Peel and chop up some soft fruit (try kiwi fruits, grapes, mangoes, or strawberries).

2 Make flavoured ice cubes from fruit squash. Whizz these in a blender to turn into crushed ice.

3 Put a layer of fruit then a layer of ice into a glass. Repeat these layers until the glass is full.

Chocolate shake

1 Put two scoops of icecream, one spoon of chocolate sauce and two cups of milk in a blender.

2 Whizz the whole mix together until blended (about 15 seconds). Pour into glasses and serve!

Bendy straw for extra fun!

Sprinkle the shake with flaked chocolate

Barbie says:

For a new flavour, try strawberry sauce instead of chocolate!

Kiwi fruit

Raspberry snow

Keep your cool when the sun is out, with this delicious recipe for Raspberry Snow! That's what I call these deep-pink ice lollies. They're made from frozen yogurt and raspberries, so they're a healthy treat on a hot day. If you don't like raspberries, try the recipe with strawberries instead. It tastes just as delicious!

You will need

Here's a cool idea!

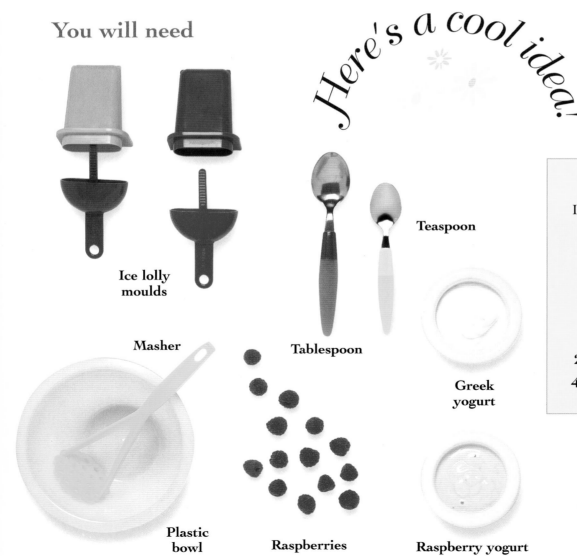

Ice lolly moulds

Masher

Teaspoon

Tablespoon

Greek yogurt

Plastic bowl

Raspberries

Raspberry yogurt

Sugar

Milk

Ingredients

If you are using strawberries instead of raspberries, remember to change the flavour of the yogurt, too!

250 g raspberries

2 tablespoons of sugar

500 g raspberry yogurt

200 g Greek yogurt

4 tablespoons of milk

1 Put the raspberries into a plastic bowl. Sprinkle them with two tablespoons of sugar.

2 Mash the fruit and sugar into a pink paste, a bit like jam. Try to get most of the lumps out.

3 Add raspberry yogurt and Greek yogurt to the plastic bowl. Give the fruity mixture a good stir.

Barbie says:

Always wash your hands and put on an apron before you start cooking!

4 Add the tablespoons of milk to the bowl, and stir them in well.

5 Spoon the mixture into ice lolly moulds. Pop them in the freezer for at least six hours.

Treat your friends! They'll think you're really cool!

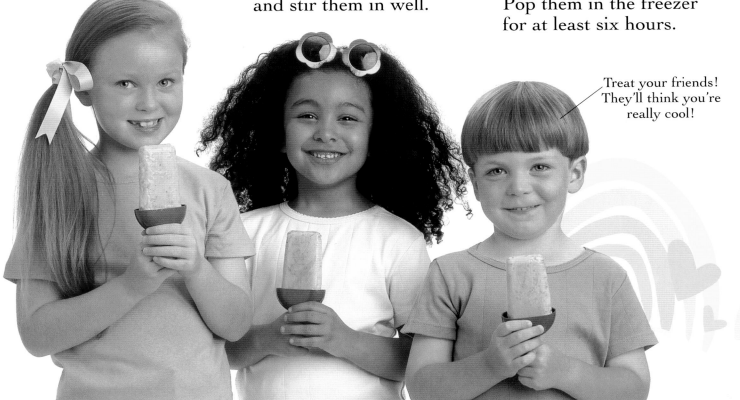

Tie-dyed T-shirt

Add a splash of colour to your wardrobe and turn a plain white T-shirt into a terrific new top when you tie-dye it. Your friends will be amazed by your new look, especially when you tell them you created it all by yourself! This activity is very messy, so make sure you ask a grown-up before you get to work.

You've got the look!

You will need

T-shirt

Cold-water dyes

Fixative

Salt

Rubber gloves

Spoon

Elastic bands

Marbles

Plastic bowl

Safety scissors

1 Tie lots of marbles into the front of your T-shirt. Hold each one in place with an elastic band.

2 Now tie marbles into both sleeves, again fixing them in place with elastic bands.

3 Using gloves, soak T-shirt in dye for about an hour (see instructions on pack for exact time).

4 Take the top out of the dye. Rinse in cold water until the water runs clean.

5 Take out the marbles. Iron the top when it's dry – then wear it!

Barbie says:
Always follow the instructions on the pack of dye!

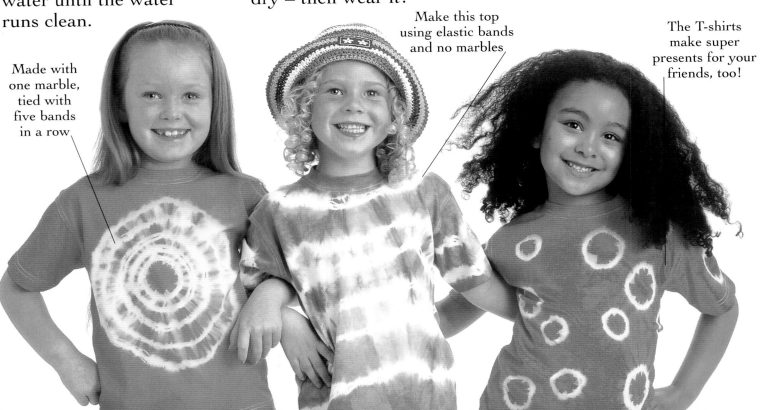

Made with one marble, tied with five bands in a row

Make this top using elastic bands and no marbles

The T-shirts make super presents for your friends, too!

Picture perfect

I love sitting down to make pictures with my little sister, Shelly. Here's a technique we think is really fun – tearing paper into squares to make a colourful mosaic. You don't need to be especially good at drawing to try this, and you won't need paints, just some old magazines and some glue! Foil sweet wrappers make great mosaics, too.

Barbie says:
You won't get sticky glue on the table if you protect your work surface with a sheet of old newspaper!

You will need

Newspaper

Pages from old magazines

Cardboard or coloured paper

Glue stick

Pen

Ruler

1 Begin your mosaic by drawing a design onto cardboard. (It's best to keep the picture simple.)

2 Choose colours for the picture. Find magazine pages with these colours; tear into small squares.

3 Working from the top and sides, put glue on part of the background; stick on the paper squares.

4 Finish the background of your mosaic first, before you start working on the main area.

5 For fine details, such as the string of this kite, put the glue on the paper square itself.

6 Make a 'frame' by sticking long strips of coloured paper around the edge of your mosaic.

This gorgeous kite is soaring in a deep blue sky

Try different designs, like this beautiful butterfly

Paper magic

Did you know that you can make "pottery" from paper? This "paper magic" is called papier mâché, and it's great fun! In the next few pages, I'll show you how to use papier mâché to make colourful plates, and a truly beautiful jewellery box.

You will need

You can make it!

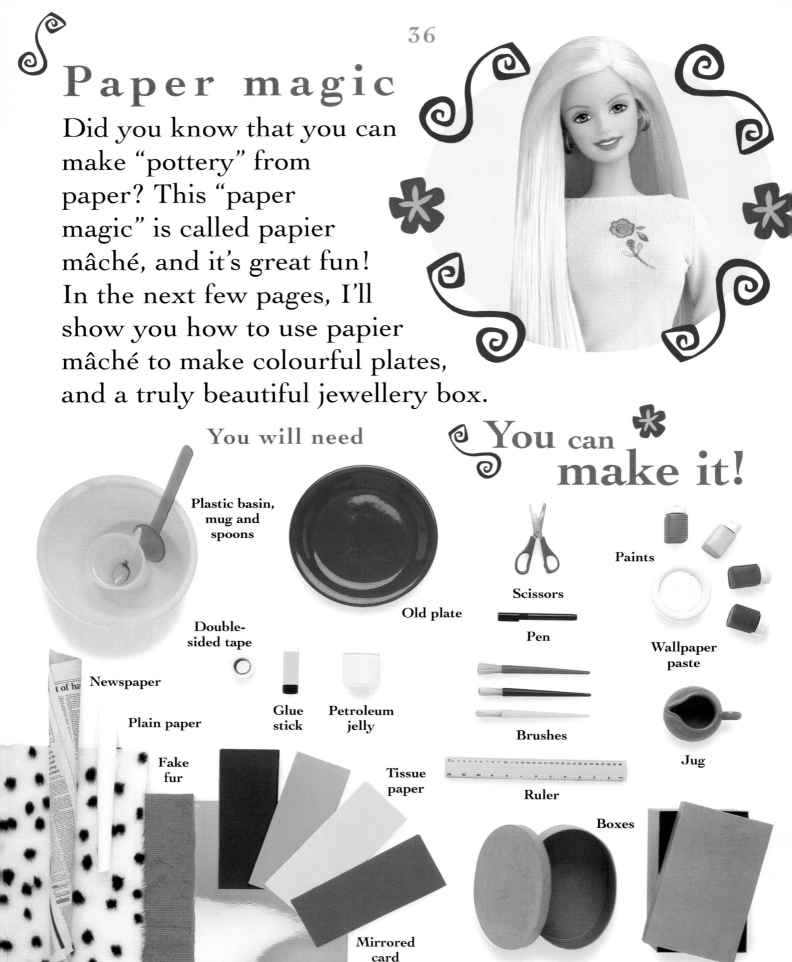

Plastic basin, mug and spoons

Old plate

Scissors

Pen

Paints

Wallpaper paste

Double-sided tape

Newspaper

Plain paper

Glue stick

Petroleum jelly

Brushes

Jug

Fake fur

Tissue paper

Ruler

Boxes

Mirrored card

Pretty plates

1 Tear sheets of old newspaper into lots of squares, each measuring about 4 cm across.

2 Thickly cover a plate with petroleum jelly. (It stops the papier mâché sticking to the plate.)

3 Cover the plate with four layers of old newspaper; paint each layer with wallpaper paste.

4 Cover newspaper with a final layer of white paper, painted with paste. Leave to dry in a warm place for at least six hours.

5 Pull the papier mâché dish away from the plate. Wipe off jelly with tissue.

6 Paste the inside of papier mâché dish, cover with a layer of white paper and paste, and leave to dry.

7 Decorate the plate with a checked pattern made from torn-up tissue paper by repeating the instructions in step 6.

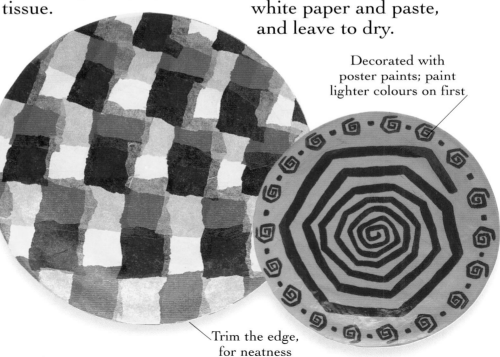

Decorated with poster paints; paint lighter colours on first

Trim the edge, for neatness

Jewellery box

1 Use a marker pen to draw a simple picture of a face in a curvy frame onto the lid of the box.

2 Tear old newspaper into thin strips. Dip in the wallpaper paste and twist them gently.

3 Lay a twist of the newspaper on top of each line of your drawing, until they are all covered.

4 To make the eyes, dip balls of paper into the paste. Squash them flat, then stick them down. Leave to dry.

5 When the papier mâché is dry, cover the lid and the face outline with two final layers of paste-and-paper squares.

Barbie says:

Protect your work surface – cover it with paper to soak up any mess!

Give your jewellery box a touch of glamour by sticking on a string of fake pearls or gemstones

6 Again, wait until the papier mâché is fully dry, then choose bright colours to paint the box and the face on top.

Just right for jewels!

Finishing off

1 Draw around the box, onto the back of some mirrored card. Cut out the shape, inside the lines.

2 If you like, draw a wiggly card frame and stick it to the "mirror", using double-sided tape.

3 Use double-sided tape to stick the mirrored card inside the lid of your jewellery box.

4 With a felt-tip pen or a marker, draw around the base of the box onto the back of some furry fabric. Cut the shape out.

5 Measure the length and depth of each side of the box. Cut out a long strip of fur to fit the sides.

6 Line the sides and base of the box with strips of double-sided sticky tape. Peel off the backing.

7 Stick the fabric, with the fur side out, inside the box. (Stick on the long side strips first, then finish with the base.)

A box of delights!

Trendy tops

How would you like to design your own T-shirt? All you will need is a plain top, some colourful fabric paints and a little inspiration! Then choose a design and start to draw. If you want to give your top the personal touch, why not paint a very special design on the T-shirt – a colourful portrait of yourself?

You make it happen!

You will need

Thick card

Plain T-shirt

Fabric paints

Plastic lid

1 Pull a T-shirt around some card; tape the sleeves back. (It's easier to draw on stretched fabric.)

2 With a fabric paint, draw around a small dish or biscuit-jar lid to make a round, face shape.

3 Add eyes and a mouth, making lots of short, light strokes with the fabric paint.

4 Now choose a paint in the same colour as your hair, to finish off your portrait.

Your self-portrait should contain all those little details that make you unique – from glasses to a bright hair ribbon!

Barbie says:

Ask a grown-up to iron your T-shirt first, so that there are no wrinkles when you paint on it.

T-shirt designs

Try designing a trendy top for a friend or someone in your family. Here are some ideas but don't be limited by them. Use your imagination!

Bicycle

Your dog

Your house

Frame it!

Do you have a favourite photo, one that reminds you of a sunny day? Perhaps it was taken during your best-ever holiday, or while you were spending a sunny afternoon in the park? Here I show you how to make a special frame for your super snap, which will always remind you of the sunshine!

You will need

Fun in the sun!

Newspaper

Bright green crêpe paper

Silk or paper flowers

Cardboard picture mounts

Blue poster paint

Strong glue

Safety scissors

Paintbrush

Fake grass fabric

Ruler

1 Paint the photo mount a bright sky blue (use a sheet of newspaper to protect your work table).

2 When the paint is dry, stick some fake grass (cut to size) to the bottom edge of the photo mount.

3 Cut out strips of green crêpe paper, about 20 x 14 cm, and roll them into narrow tubes.

4 Glue along one edge of the stems; stick them to the sides of the frame.

5 Glue silk or paper flowers on the stems (also see pages 18 to 21).

Barbie says:

Make a frame with a seaside theme, too! Here's one for you to copy!

Paint on a fluffy cloud

Tape your sunshine photo to the back of the photo frame

Starfish give a "seaside" feel

Sprinkle on glitter when the paint is still wet

This paint has been mixed with a little sand

Kiss and make-up

One great way to have fun with your friends is to paint gorgeous pictures on each others' faces! The summery design I show here is a mix of flowers and honey bees. Make sure you buy water-based face paints. They are easy to put on, and they wash off easily, too. And if you have long hair, tie it back – a headband is ideal.

You will need

Water-based face paints

Glitter

Face gel

Now let's get started!

Barbie says:

Ask a grown-up first if it's OK to paint your friend's face!

Paintbrushes

Cup of water

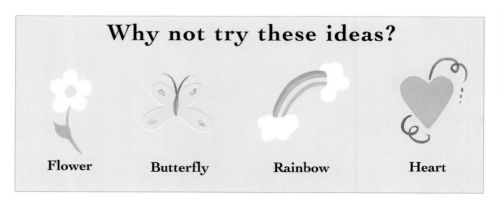

Why not try these ideas?

Flower   **Butterfly**   **Rainbow**   **Heart**

Flowers

1 With a flat brush, paint yellow circles on your friend's face – these are the middle of the flowers.

2 Paint on some pretty purple petals. Don't forget to wash the brush between each colour.

3 Add curly green stalks to link each flower. Finish off with dots of gel mixed with glitter.

Bumble bees

1 Begin by choosing a flat brush to paint small, round bumble bee bodies on to your friend's cheeks or forehead.

2 Carefully draw wing shapes with white paint on each bee. Wash the brush.

3 Use black paint to add stripes, eyes and little stalks onto your bee.

4 Paint tiny white spirals under your bee, to make it look as if it is buzzing through the air!

Friendship bracelets

Show your friend how much she means to you by making her a friendship bracelet. All you need are some beads and some strands of wool – choose them in your friend's favourite colours, or to match her best outfit. I'll show you how easy it is to weave the strands together and thread the beads. Have fun!

You will need

Wool threads

Beads

Safety scissors

How to weave a friendship bracelet

Start from the left.
Put thread 1 over
thread 2.

Now pull thread
1 underneath
thread 3

Finally, put
thread 1 over
thread 4.

Pull tight and start
again (begin with
the new thread 1).

1 Take four coloured threads, 50 cm long. Fold them in half; tie a knot in the folded end to make a loop.

2 Keeping the loop at the top, separate the threads out into their four different colours.

3 Give the loop to your friend to hold. (Or tape the loop to a plastic surface to hold it steady.)

4 Start with the thread on the left. Weave it across the other threads (see box); pull it tight.

Barbie says:

Tie to your friend's wrist by threading the finished end through the loop.

Best of friends!

5 Keep weaving the threads until you are 3 cm from the end. Now thread on the beads and knot the ends of thread.

The finished bracelet looks great!

Helpful hints

There are a few extra tips on this page that will help you with the fun-to-make activities in this book.

Making holes

1 You can make holes in paper or card with a ball of modelling clay and a sharp pencil.

2 Put the clay on a table, with the card on top. Press the pencil into the clay, making a neat hole.

Drawing a circle

1 Knot a long piece of string tightly around a sharp pencil, just above the tip, as shown.

2 For a 20 cm circle, put a pin in the string, 10 cm (half of 20) from the pencil (adapt as needed.)

3 Pin the string to some paper. Keep the thread tight as you pull the pencil round in a circle.

Copying patterns

1 Ask a grown-up to photocopy and enlarge the pattern you need, at the required size.

2 Copy the pattern onto tracing paper. Turn the paper over; rub a pencil underneath the outline.

3 Turn back to the traced outline; draw over it again, onto either card or paper, as required.